# oliv

*recipes & remedies*

## Contents

Text by Alan Charles.

This edition published in 2008 by L&K Designs.
© L&K Designs 2008
Printed in China

Publisher's Disclaimer

The uses, hints, tips and ideas contained in this book are passed on in good faith but the publisher cannot be held responsible for any adverse results.

Please be aware that certain recipes may contain nuts.

# Introduction

Olives are thought to have originated in Crete between five and seven thousand years ago and consumed since as early as 3,000 B.C. Since ancient times, the olive tree has provided food, fuel, timber and medicine for many civilizations, and has been regarded as a symbol of peace and wisdom.

Olive oil has been, and still is a staple ingredient in the diet of many Mediterranean countries. It is a natural juice that preserves the taste, aroma, vitamins and other properties of the olive fruit. Olive oil is the only vegetable oil that can be consumed as is, freshly pressed from the fruit itself.

Nowadays, olive oil is being rediscovered as a delicious and nutritious addition to our daily diets. Science has finally noticed what others have instinctively known for hundreds of years; olive oil doesn't just taste good, it's actually really good for you!

Recent studies have found that the Mediterranean diet may be linked to a reduced risk of heart disease and other health conditions. These studies have been the basis for olive oil becoming increasingly popular throughout the World over the past few decades.

Today, much of the commercial cultivation of olive oil is still centered in the Mediterranean region in such countries as Spain, Italy, Greece, Portugal and Turkey. However, more and more countries from across the world are including olive oil on their list of exports.

Olive oils are as diverse as wines; there are approximately 700 cultivated varieties of olives. The oils derived from them can be anywhere from mellow yellow in colour to light green. The taste can be peppery, sweet and buttery, nutty, grassy, or it can taste like green apples.

Although olive oil is chiefly used as a food or in food preservation, it is also used in today's society in soaps, pharmaceuticals and cosmetics. You can enjoy the benefits of olive oil in everything from dips and dressings, to skin care and shampoo.

As well as exploring the many ways in which olive oil can be used in the kitchen for recipes, this book looks at the many uses of olive oil, from household hints to health & beauty tips, so you can get the most from this increasingly popular super-food.

Olives &
Olive Oil

# Olives & Olive Oil

The olive (Olea europaea) dates back to 17th century B.C where it first appeared in print in Egyptian records and was mentioned numerous times in the Bible. The word comes from the Latin olivea which first appeared in the English language around 1200 a.d.

## The Olive Tree

Olive trees are the oldest fruit trees and certainly one of the most important fruit trees in history. Olive tree culture has been closely connected to the rise and fall of Mediterranean empires and other advanced civilizations throughout the ages. Because olive trees offered wealth and future food supplies to established civilizations, the agricultural nations became stable societies, resulting from a secure expectation from past experience of an uninterrupted food and olive oil supply. This factor was a necessary requirement for population growth and increase.

Dependable fruit production and olive oil production means that olive trees must exist in a stable society and a peaceful environment. That stability must extend for many years, since most ancient seedling olive trees required eight or more years before ever producing the first crop of fruit.

Medical properties of olive oil were reported by many ancient Greek writers and philosophers, their importance in creating nutritional benefits and wealth for Greek citizens continues abundantly today - some Greek olive tree orchards contain a million or more trees.

The fragrant flowers of olive trees are small and creamy white, hidden within the thick leaves. The blossoms usually begin appearing in April and can continue for many months. A wild, seedling olive tree normally begins to flower and produce fruit at the age of 8 years. The fruit of the olive tree is a purplish-black when completely ripe, but a few cultivars are green when ripe and some olives turn a colour of copper-brown.

The size of the olive fruit is variable, even on the same tree, and the shape ranges from round to oval with pointed ends. Some olives can be eaten fresh after sun-drying and the taste is sweet, but most olive cultivars are bitter and must be treated by various chemical solutions before developing into edible olives. If the olives are thinned on the limbs of the trees to 2 or 3 per twig, the ultimate size of the olives will be much larger. The fruit is gathered in mid October and should be processed as soon as possible to prevent fermentation and a decline in quality.

The leaves of olive trees are gray-green and are replaced at 2-3 year intervals during the spring after new growth appears. Pruning yearly and severely is very important to insure continued production.

The trees have the unproductive limbs removed so that it will be more fruitful. An olive tree can grow to 50 feet with a limb spread of 30 feet, but most growers will keep the tree pruned to 20 feet to assure maximum production. New sprouts and trees will emerge from the olive tree stump roots, even if the trees are cut down. Some olive trees are believed to be over a thousand years old, and most will live to the ripe old age of 500 years.

Olives generally are beaten off trees with poles, harvested mechanically or by shaking the fruit from the trees onto canvas. Most ripening olives are removed from the trees after the majority of the fruit begins to change in colour. It is important to squeeze out the olive oil within a day after harvesting or else fermentation or decline in flavour and quality will occur. The olive oil can be consumed or used in cooking immediately after its collection from the press.

Olive oils are unique and distinct, each brand of olive oil having its own character, as determined by many factors, like those unique flavour differences found in fine wines. Prepared commercial olive oils can vary greatly in aroma, fruit flavour; whether the taste is flowery, nutty, delicate, or mild, and the colouring of olive oil is quite variable.

# Types of Olives

The only difference between green olives and black olives is ripeness, unripe olives are green and fully ripe olives are black. Olives are cured or pickled before consumption, using various methods including oil-cured, water-cured, brine-cured, dry-cured, and lye-cured.

Green olives must be soaked in a lye solution before brining, whereas ripe black olives can proceed straight to brining. The longer the olive is permitted to ferment in its own brine, the less bitter and more intricate its flavour will become. Green olives are usually pitted, and often stuffed with various fillings, including pimientos, almonds, anchovies, jalapeños, onions or capers.

Black olives are graded into sizes labelled as small, medium, large, extra large, jumbo, colossal, and super-colossal. Black olives contain more oil than green. Unopened olives can be stored at room temperature up to two years. Opened olives should be refrigerated in their own liquid in a non-metal container and will last up to several weeks after opening.

Here are some of the more popular olive varieties:

### Anzanilla
Spanish green olive, available un-pitted and/or stuffed, lightly lye-cured then packed in salt and lactic acid brine.

### Picholine
French green olive, salt-brine cured, with subtle, lightly salty flavour.

### Kalamata
Greek black olive, harvested fully ripe, deep purple, almond-shaped, brine-cured, rich and fruity flavour.

### Niçoise
French black olive, harvested fully ripe, small in size, rich, nutty, mellow flavour, high pit-to-meat ratio, often packed with herbs and stems intact.

**Liguria**
Italian black olive, salt-brine cured, with a vibrant flavour, sometimes packed with stems.

**Ponentine**
Italian black olive, salt-brine cured then packed in vinegar, mild in flavour.

**Gaeta**
Italian black olive, dry-salt cured, then rubbed with oil, wrinkled in appearance, mild flavour, often packed with rosemary and other herbs.

**Lugano**
Italian black olive, usually very salty, sometimes packed with olive leaves, popular at tastings.

**Sevillano**
Californian, salt-brine cured and preserved with lactic acid, very crisp.

## Olive Oil Properties

Sun, stone, drought, silence and solitude: these are the five ingredients that, according to Italian folk traditions, create the ideal habitat for the olive tree.

Climate, soil, variety of tree and time of harvest account for the different organoleptic properties of different oils. Certain extra virgin olive oils are blends of varieties of olives; others are made from one variety of tree.

The price of extra virgin olive oil varies greatly. Two factors are influential: where the olives are grown and which harvesting methods are implemented. Certain locations yield more bountiful harvests; consequently their oil is sold for less. Olive trees planted near the sea can produce up to 20 times more fruit than those planted inland, in hilly areas like Tuscany. It is in these land-locked areas that the olive trees' habitat is pushed to the extreme; if the conditions were just a little more severe, the trees would not survive. Extra virgin oils produced from these trees have higher organoleptic scores.

## Types of Olive Oil

Olive oil is highly-prized not only for its health benefits, but also for its wonderful flavour. The best oil is a blend of oil from a mixture of red-ripe (not green and not fully ripe) olives and a smaller proportion of oil from green olives of a different variety.

Generally, olive oil is extracted by pressing or crushing olives. Cold-pressing, a chemical-free process using only pressure, produces a higher quality of olive oil which is naturally lower in acidity. The oil that comes from the first "pressing" of the olive, is extracted without using heat or chemicals, and has no "off" flavours is awarded "extra virgin" status. The less the olive oil is handled, the closer to its natural state, the better the oil. If the olive oil meets all the criteria, it can be designated as "extra virgin".

When purchasing olive oil, it's important to check labels for the percentage of acidity, grade of oil, volume, and country of origin. The level of acidity is a key factor in choosing fine olive oil, along with colour, flavour and aroma. Here are the different types of olive oil:

### Extra Virgin Olive Oil

Considered the best, least processed, comprising the oil from the first cold-pressing of the olives, with only 1% acid; considered the finest and fruitiest, and thus the most expensive; ranges from a crystalline champagne colour to greenish-golden to bright green; generally, the deeper the colour, the more intense the olive flavour. Cooking with this oil at a high temperature loses some flavour but doesn't change the basics of the oil. Use expensive olive oil when cooking with high heat. Also used well as last second touches to dishes and they make a great addition to tomato sauces, dressings and in marinades. Fine restaurants use it so you can dip crustier breads for a simple appetizer.

### Virgin Olive Oil

The olives are pressed beyond their usual means and chemicals are used to further extra oils. They're typically mixed with oils from other provinces to reintroduce the flavours lost from the process. Virgin olive oil, cooking in the same way as the extra virgin. It's also used as a condiment a lot of times due to its aroma and taste and is more reasonably priced than the extra virgin makes it more accessible for use and is great for high-heat cooking. Also

a first-press oil, with a slightly higher acidity level of between 1-3%.

### Fino Olive Oil

Fino (Meaning fine in Italian) is a blend of extra virgin and virgin olive oils.

### Pure Olive Oil

Pure olive oil means that it's only olive oil, nothing else is mixed with it. The process used to make it removes the flavour. Olive oil is added in the end to give it a bit of flavour and slight aroma. Use this for your majority of cooking as the heat removes the flavour and aroma anyway and it's more cost-effective. It's very suitable for high temperature cooking as the refining process increases its smoking point.

### Light Olive Oil

This version contains the same amount of beneficial monounsaturated fats as regular olive oil, but due to the refining process, it is lighter in colour and has essentially no flavour. This makes it a good choice for baking and other purposes where the heavy flavour might not be desirable. The olive oils are all perfect for your cooking needs giving the consumer high smoking points and flavours that mingle making these oils incredibly versatile. They are best suited for high heat cooking or as an alternative to butter (or other oil types when baking, like vegetable oil). You will require less olive oil when replacing butter (at 3 tablespoons per 1/4 cup of butter). Mild or light oils are great for those who want a very light olive taste but maintaining the health benefits.

### Extra Light Olive Oil

Undergoes considerable processing and only retains a very mild olive flavour.

## Storing Your Olive Oil

Since olive oil can become rancid from exposure to light and heat, there are some important purchasing criteria you should follow to ensure buying a better quality product. Look for olive oils that are sold in dark tinted bottles since the packaging will help protect the oil from exposure to light. In addition, make sure the oil is displayed in a cool area, away from any direct or indirect contact with heat.

Proper storage techniques for olive oil are very important, not only to preserve the delicate taste of the oil, but also to ensure that it does not spoil and become rancid, which will have a negative effect on its nutritional profile.

If purchasing oil in tinted glass containers, choose those at the back of the supermarket shelf out of direct light. Buy your olive oil in smaller containers and store in a cool, dark place for up to six months or in the refrigerator up to a year. Leaving a bottle of olive oil out on your kitchen counter or dining room table will lessen its health-giving properties.

Check the label for a bottling date for freshness. Olive oil does not improve with age like fine wine and is best when used during the first six months of pressing.

Refrigerated or very cold olive oil will become cloudy, but will clear up when brought to room temperature. Be sure it's kept in an airtight container. Use higher quality forms of olive oil for flavour foremost, and lower grades for high-heat cooking applications.

# Health Benefits of Olive Oil

Olive oil produces many health benefits when used in cooking or when poured over salads. The use of olive oil can improve digestion and can benefit heart metabolism through its low content of cholesterol. Experts claim that olive oil consumption will cause a person to grow shiny hair, prevent dandruff, prevent wrinkles, prevent dry skin and acne, strengthen nails, stop muscle aching, lower blood pressure and cancel out the effects of alcohol.

Research has shown that heart disease is dramatically lower in Mediterranean countries where olive oil is a dietary staple than areas where consumption of olive oil is less voracious. Science has now determined that olive oil, as a monounsaturated fat, increases HDL or good blood cholesterol. However, it is still important to remember that olive oil is still a fat and should be consumed in limited quantities, in proper ratio to your balanced diet.

We treasure extra-virgin olive oil for its nutritional and salutary virtues. It is the most digestible of the edible fats: it helps to assimilate vitamins A, D and K; it contains so-called essential acids that cannot be produced by our own bodies; it slows down the aging process; and it helps bile, liver and intestinal functions. It is also valued for its culinary virtues and organoleptic properties as well: flavour, bouquet and colour.

# Cooking Techniques

### Sautéing

One of the highest of the high heat cooking methods and one of the most suited for your light and mild olive oils. In French, sautéing translates as "jump", an indication that the food literally jumps in the pan from the heat. It's a very fast method of cooking and is stir-frying without a wok.

### Pan-Frying

Pan-frying with olive oil preserves the taste of the meat and vegetables. You use more oil than you do with sautéing and cook at a lower heat.

## Deep-Frying

Olive oil is not regularly used for this method. Vegetable oil, soy and peanut oil are typically the desired oils to use. Your standard pure olive oil is best for deep-frying if you choose to use it.

## Stir-Frying

The Oriental way of sautéing is stir-frying and like sautéing, it demands a high temperature in which to cook your food. The pan varies however, having very high sides and dents in them that cling to the food. Again, pure olive is best used in the case. Oriental cooking likes to maintain the flavours of the meats and vegetables and too much of an olive oil taste would ruin, in their eyes, an otherwise great dish.

Everyday Hints
& Tips

# Everyday Hints & Tips

Olive oil is a great ingredient in the kitchen. It can be drizzled over salads, used as part of a recipe for sauces, and used to cook meats and vegetables with. However, cooking isn't the only thing that olive oil can be used for.

In fact, it can be used for a whole variety of things that you've probably never even thought of. Anything that requires oil, moisturiser or some shine might benefit from a little dab of olive oil. Here are just some of the great uses for olive oil for around the house that don't have anything to do with cooking:

## Household

### Furniture Polish

Combine 2 parts olive oil and 1 part lemon juice or white vinegar in a clean recycled spray bottle, shake it up, and spray it on. Leave the mixture on for a minute or two, then wipe off with a clean cloth or kitchen roll.

In a hurry? Get fast results by applying olive oil straight from the bottle onto kitchen roll. Wipe off the excess with another piece of kitchen roll or an absorbent cloth.

## Wood Polish

Melted with some beeswax and poured into a small tin, olive oil makes a great wood polish that can be used on all different types of wood throughout your home. It will nourish your furniture while it polishes too.

## Silence Squeaky Doors

Lubricate squeaky door and cupboard hinges by applying a small dab of olive oil onto a cloth, wiping across the top of the hinges so that the oil runs down the sides.

## Eliminate Wax From Candle Holders

Rub a thin coat of olive oil into your holders before you burn candles and dripped wax should peel away easily.

## Shine Stainless Steel

Many cleaning products such as ammonia can dull and even corrode chrome and stainless steel. Olive oil, however, is a safe and effective shining agent. Great for cleaning stainless steel kitchen appliances or utensils.

## Floor Polish

Mix 3 parts olive oil with one part white vinegar for wood floor polish. Apply and rub in well.

## Garden Tools

Coat garden tool blades with a thin layer of olive oil to prevent dirt sticking to them and to help prevent them from rusting.

## Brass

To keep brass looking shinier for longer, buff with olive oil after cleaning, this keeps it from tarnishing so fast.

# Pets

## Cats

Add 1/8 to 1/4 teaspoon to your cat's food to help prevent hair balls.

## Dogs

Add one teaspoon of olive oil to your dog's food on a weekly basis to help it shed less fur than normal.

# Clothing

## Unstick A Zip

Apply a small drop of olive oil onto the zip to lubricate the teeth (avoid touching the fabric.) The zip should then move up and down freely.

## Restore Leather

To help prevent cracking and hardening of leather shoes or to simply improve the softness of leather gloves, occasionally rub in a little olive oil to give them a second lease on life.

# Kitchen

### Basting

Rub olive oil onto chicken or turkey instead of butter when roasting.

### Garlic Bread

Mix olive oil in with butter and garlic for your garlic bread, a fantastic combination.

### Roast Garlic

Cut the top off a whole head of garlic, sprinkle it with salt and pepper and drizzle olive oil over the top. Wrap it up in foil and roast in the oven until the garlic gets soft. Tastes fantastic spread over a slice of bread.

### A Replacement For Butter
Put a ramekin of olive oil in the fridge and it develops the same consistency as butter. A healthier alternative to butter too.

### Frying Pans
Recycle a spray bottle and fill with plain or flavoured olive oil to use as a spray. Spray your pans before cooking.

### A Bread Dip
Olive oil makes the perfect dip for dunking bread in, especially if mixed with balsamic vinegar.

## Body

### Removing Paint From Skin
Rub some olive oil onto the affected area and let it soak a while then rinse well with soap. The paint usually comes off without the need for any skin damaging materials. The olive oil will also leave your skin feeling soft.

### Remove Paint From Hair
Moisten a cotton ball with some olive oil and gently rub it into your hair, then shampoo well afterwards to wash out the oil.

### Rings
Instead of using washing up liquid as a lubricant to remove rings stuck on fingers, a drizzle of olive oil on the ring will help in just the same way.

### Nappy Rash
Gently wipe olive oil onto your baby's bottom to help sooth the irritation of nappy rash.

### Snoring
A sip of olive oil just before you go to sleep makes the throat slippery and should be enough to stop you or your partner snoring.

### Scalp Conditioner

To condition bald heads, simply rub the scalp with olive oil and then lay on a hot (not burning), moist towel. When the towel cools, reheat in the microwave being careful not to get too hot. Continue doing this several times.

### Massage Oil

Not only does olive oil work perfectly as a lubricant for reflexology or massages, it also leaves your skin feeling soft and moisturised.

Health & Beauty

# Health Hints & Tips

As with most cooking oils, olive oil contains about 120 calories per tablespoon. However, unlike the others, olive oil is a very good source of vitamin A and E, an antioxidant, which helps to neutralise cancer-causing agents in our bodies.

It is mono unsaturated, therefore it lowers the "bad" LDL cholesterol without reducing the "good" HDL cholesterol. This results in improved circulation, lowered blood pressure and less risk of heart disease.

It is a great source of nourishment because of the great quantities of vitamins, iron, sodium and potassium it contains. Its high concentration of oleic acid not only keeps our arteries supple, it is also partly responsible for olive oil's popularity.

One particular study concluded that with only two tablespoons of virgin olive oil every day, you can begin to experience the health benefits that Mediterranean people have enjoyed for so many years.

Olive oil has been linked with improving many health conditions, including the following:

## Constipation
Take one tablespoon of olive oil at bedtime or better yet on an empty stomach.

## Diarrhoea
Mix one teaspoon of olive oil, one teaspoon of red wine, one teaspoon of rose water and take twice a day, in the morning and at bedtime.

## Hepatic Infections
One teaspoon of olive oil mixed with 5 drops of lemon juice on an empty stomach and before bedtime.

## Psoriasis
Mix 2 teaspoons of olive oil with a large glass of milk and add to your bathwater to ease the outbreak.

## Blood Pressure
With the fast pace of the modern day lifestyle and the stresses and strains that come with it, a daily dose of olive oil helps to reduce the body's blood pressure levels.

### Reduction of Cholesterol
The mono unsaturated fatty acids in olive oil controls LDL (bad cholesterol) and enhances HDL (good cholesterol), helping to balance out the bodies' cholesterol levels.

### Colon Cancer
Studies in Spain have discovered that olive oil can help towards the reduction and prevention of colon cancer amongst many other forms of this disease.

### Thrombosis & Arteriosclerosis
It is said that olive oil could possibly help the prevention and cure of diseases like thrombosis and arteriosclerosis.

### Helps The Digestive Track
Properties found in olive oil help ease the intestinal functions by activating the secretion of bile and other hormones.

### Coronary Artery Diseases
Olive oil is great for cardiovascular and coronary artery diseases. Blood reaches the heart through coronary arteries. The mono unsaturated fats in olive oil clears the arteries and enables the smooth supply of oxygen and nutrients.

### Gall Bladder
Olive oil has been known to help with the stimulation of the gall bladder.

### Promoting Cellular Growth
Cellular growth is improved with a daily diet of olive oil, which speeds healing and helps the body's metabolism.

### Aging
Olive oil is said to help slow down the aging process.

### Arthritis
Topical use of extra virgin can help alleviate arthritis.

### Diabetes

Olive oil helps to reduce the body's blood sugar levels, in turn helping to fight off diabetes.

### Vitamins

Olive oil has been proven to help increase the absorption of vital vitamins such as A, D and K.

### Burns

Olive oil is often used for relief from burns and inflammations to the skin.

### Skin Relief

It helps relieve itches, stings and insect bites.

### Earache

Pour the olive oil into your ear, add a cotton ball to keep the oil in your ear and relax while it works its magic.

### Sore Throat

A sip of olive oil will help stop a sore throat or those annoying tickling coughs.

### Treat Hair Lice

Olive oil is a safe and healthy remedy for killing head lice. Cover the hair in olive oil and wrap it up in a plastic bag leaving it on your head for approximately 8 hours, then shampoo out. It might take 2 shampoos to get all the oil out of your hair. The olive oil will kill the head lice, however, it won't kill the eggs. You will need to comb the eggs out with a head lice comb, but because the hair becomes really soft from the olive oil treatment, the eggs will come out much easier.

# Beauty Hints & Tips

Olive oil is one of those magical substances that is good for almost everything - your diet, your skin, your hair and your hands and nails. Prized for its cosmetic uses since ancient times, olive oil is relatively inexpensive and can be purchased in most supermarkets.

Use extra virgin, as brands labelled "pure" and "light" have been chemically processed. Because the oil's fat composition is very similar to that of human skin, it rarely causes allergic reactions. In addition, it's absorbed quickly and helps lock in moisture in the skin. The high percentage of unsaturated fat and vitamins A and E, helpful in preventing sun damage, also work on the outside to soothe and replenish, particularly sensitive skin. It is also pure, and unmixed with anything but water, unlike other oils.

Buy yourself an attractive storage bottle to keep olive oil in, you can then keep it in the bathroom rather than dragging the big container out of the kitchen every night. And if you don't like the smell, you can always mix it with a little of your favourite hand, body, or hair lotions.

# Hair

### For Brittle Hair

For brittle or over-processed hair, rinse your hair after a shampoo with a solution of olive oil and egg (one beaten egg with 1/2 to 3/4 cup of olive oil) and leaving it on 30-45 minutes, covered with a plastic cap. Weekly or monthly treatments are recommended depending on the condition of your hair.

### To Thicken Hair

To help thicken hair, soak your locks in 1/2 to 3/4 cup of warm olive oil and wrap them in a towel for 30 minutes.

### Cure/Prevent Oily Hair

Balance out the natural oils produced by your hair by using olive oil to regulate your oil secretion. Simply rub a dab of olive oil on your scalp before bed and oily hair will start to calm down.

### Hair Conditioner

Put the moisture back into your hair by heating 1/2 cup olive oil (don't boil it), and then applying it liberally to your hair. Cover your hair with a plastic bag, then wrap it in a towel. Let it set for 45 minutes, then shampoo out the olive oil and rinse thoroughly.

### Frizzy Hair

Not only does olive oil condition hair, but it also gets rid of frizziness. Put a small drop into the palm of your hand, rub your hands together and apply to dry hair.

### Static Hair

Rub olive oil into your hands and run your finger tips through your hair. Follow with a brush to help reduce static hair.

### Removing Chewing Gum From Hair

Rub the olive oil into the chewing gum and affected strands of hair. Keep rubbing until the strands become separated, then shampoo and rinse off.

# Face

## Lips

To soothe and smooth dry, chapped lips, dab a little olive oil onto them. Melted with some beeswax and poured into a small tin, olive oil makes great lip balm.

## Face

Whenever your face needs softening and moisturising, massage a small amount of olive oil into your skin, applying extra oil to rough or cracked areas.

## Facial

For an exfoliating facial, wet face thoroughly, then massage olive oil into your skin. Use about a half teaspoon of sugar and scrub your face, then wipe off gently with a warm, wet cloth until the sugar is all gone.

## Face Mask

Take one tablespoon of olive oil and mix with 2 tablespoons of fresh cream, leave it on the face for 10 minutes and then wash your face with warm water. Mix 1 tablespoon of honey with 15 drops of orange juice and one tablespoon of Fullers Earth cream and add one tablespoon of rose water. Mix well and apply on the face, wash off after 10 minutes.

### Makeup/Mascara Remover

Dab a little olive oil on a cotton swab or tissue to remove makeup. It is as good as any high street cosmetic brand at removing mascara.

### Remove Eye Liner/Makeup

Dab a little under the eyes and rinse off with a washcloth.

### Clear Up Acne

Make a paste by mixing 4 tablespoons of salt with 3 tablespoons of olive oil. Pour the mixture into your hands and work it around your face. Leave it on for 2 minutes, then rinse it off with warm, soapy water. Apply daily for one week, then cut back to two or three times weekly. You should see a noticeable improvement in your condition. The principle is that the salt cleanses the pores by exfoliation, while the olive oil restores the skin's natural moisture.

### Shaving

People with sensitive skin can use olive oil as a shaving cream. It not only makes it easier for the blade to glide over your face or legs, but it will moisturise your skin as well.

# Body

## Olive Oil As An Ingredient

Look for olive oil in lip balms, shampoos, bath oils, hand lotions, soaps, soaks for nails, massage oils, and dandruff treatments.

## Beautify Your Skin

You can use olive oil as a skin lotion to soften skin. Or you can add some to your bath to get a silky smooth feeling. In all these ways, olive oil improves the appearance and feel of your skin. Essential oils, such as lavender or jasmine will provide a touch of fragrance to your olive oil bath soak.

## Daily Moisturiser

Rub a thin layer over the skin after a shower or a waxing to help treat dry skin.

## Body Exfoliator

For an invigorating body, face or foot scrub, rub olive oil into the skin and scrub with sugar.

# Hands & Feet

## Hands

To soften your hands, smooth on a generous amount of olive oil before bed, put on white cotton gloves, and sleep with them on.

## Moisturise Cuticles

For ragged cuticles, apply a small amount of olive oil to the nail beds. This will soften the cuticles so you can safely push them back.

## Brittle Nails

For brittle nails, soak your nails in a small bowl of warm olive oil (add a squeeze of lemon for a nicer scent). A few minutes' dunking can help brittle nails become more resilient.

## Clean Greasy Hands

To remove car grease or paint from your hands, pour one teaspoon of olive oil and one teaspoon of salt or sugar into the palms of your hands. Vigorously rub the mixture into your hands and between your fingers for several minutes; then wash it off with soap and water. Not only will your hands be cleaner, they'll be softer too.

## Feet

Take one cup of lemon juice, 2 tablespoons of olive oil, cinnamon, 1/4 cup of milk and dilute with water to make a wash that leaves skin refreshed and fragrant. Once you have made it, you can put it in a tub where you can soak your feet or body. Then dry your feet or rinse them with water and a mild soap. After a few weeks of doing this your skin will feel silky smooth.

Starters & Salads

# Starters

## Olive Paste (serves 6-8)

*Ingredients*
225g/8oz of kalamata or mixed green and black olives
1 medium onion, chopped
3 tablespoons of capers, rinsed
1 tablespoon of chopped fresh oregano or 1 to 1/2 teaspoon of dried oregano
3 tablespoons of olive oil
2 tablespoons of red wine vinegar
grated peel (no white attached) of 1 lemon
1/2 teaspoon of freshly ground black pepper

*Preparation*
Place the olives in a colander and rinse thoroughly under cold running water. Remove the pits from the olives and discard.

In the bowl of a food processor, combine the pitted olives, onion, capers, oregano, olive oil, vinegar, and lemon peel. Process to a spreading consistency. Season to taste with the pepper and store in a small jar in the refrigerator.

# Taramasalata (serves 6-8)

This classic Greek dish is a favourite all over the world, and served best with warm pitta bread.

*Ingredients*
2 large old potatoes, peeled
120g/4oz of cod's roe or tarama
75ml/2 1/2fl oz of lemon juice
150ml/5fl oz of extra virgin olive oil
2 tablespoons of fresh parsley

*Preparation*
Cut the potatoes into 2cm cubes. Place into small pan; cover with water. Bring to the boil, reduce heat and simmer; covered for 15 minutes or until tender. Drain well. Mash the potato with a fork until almost smooth then allow to cool. Using electric beaters, beat the roe in small mixing bowl on high speed for 2 minutes. Add the potato gradually, beating thoroughly after each addition.

Add the juice and oil gradually, beating thoroughly after each addition. When all the oil and juice has been added, beat the mixture on a high speed for 5 minutes or until light and fluffy.

Refrigerate for 2 hours. Finely chop the parsley. Transfer the puree into a serving dish; sprinkle with parsley. Serve at room temperature with bread and olives.

# Caper & Olive Oil Tapenade (serves 6-8)

*Ingredients*
5 tablespoons of capers
115g/4oz of green olives
2 flat anchovy fillets - more as required
4 garlic cloves
115ml/4fl oz of extra virgin olive oil

*Preparation*
Coarsely chop the ingredients or blend in a food processor.  Spoon over slices of French bread or use as a dip.

# Olive Oil Crackers (serves 6-8)

If you have trouble tracking down semolina flour, just substitute white whole wheat flour (or all-purpose flour), it will make a slightly different cracker but should still work. To get creative with your crackers you can top them with lots of things before baking: freshly grated cheese, artisan salts, a dusting of your favourite spice blend, seeds, or a wash of your favorite flavoured or infused oil. You can simply cut the unbaked cracker dough into various shapes using one of those pizza cutting wheels.

*Ingredients*
330g/12oz of semolina flour
330g/12oz of white whole wheat flour (or all-purpose flour)
1 tablespoon of fine-grain sea salt
225ml/7 1/2fl oz of warm water
75ml/2 1/2fl oz of extra virgin olive oil

*Equipment*
Pasta machine (optional)

*Preparation*
Whisk together the flours and salt. Add the water and olive oil. Using a mixer with a dough hook attachment mix the dough at medium speed for about 5

to 7 minutes. Alternatively, feel free to mix and then knead by hand on a floured kitchen worktop. The dough should be just a bit tacky - not too dry, not too sticky to work with. If you need to add a bit more water (or flour) do so.

When you are done mixing, shape the dough into a large ball. Now cut into twelve equal-sized pieces. Gently rub each piece with a bit of olive oil, shape into a small ball and place on a plate. Cover with a clean dishtowel or plastic wrap and let rest at room temperature for 30 - 60 minutes.

While the dough is resting, preheat your oven to 230°C degrees. Insert a pizza stone if you have one.

When the dough is done resting, flatten one dough ball. Using a rolling pin or a pasta machine, shape into a flat strip of dough. You can also cut the dough into whatever shape you like at this point. Set dough on a floured (or cornmeal dusted) baking sheet, poke each cracker with a fork to prevent puffing, add any extra toppings, and slide into the oven (onto the pizza stone). Repeat the process for the remaining dough balls, baking in small batches. If you don't have a pizza stone, bake crackers a few at a time on baking sheets.

Bake until deeply golden, and let cool before eating - you will get more crackery snap. Makes a dozen extra large crackers.

# Tomato & Basil Bruschetta (serves 4)

*Ingredients*
6 tomatoes, diced
2 cloves of garlic, chopped
2 cloves of garlic, peeled
3 tablespoons of olive oil
2 1/4 teaspoons of balsamic vinegar
2 tablespoons of chopped fresh basil
1/2 teaspoon of sea salt
1/4 teaspoon of fresh cracked pepper
8 slices of Italian bread, cut about 1 inch thick
2 tablespoons of grated parmesan cheese

*Preparation*
Whisk together the chopped garlic, vinegar, salt, pepper and basil. When combined slowly drizzle in oil. Add tomatoes and let sit for 20 minutes at room temp.

Meanwhile, toast the bread. This can be done either in the toaster or the grill. When the bread is toasted rub each piece, on one side, with the whole garlic pieces. Place the bread on a baking sheet and top with tomato mixture.

Sprinkle on a little cheese and grill until the cheese melts.

Serve immediately.

The tomato mixture also makes a wonderful vinaigrette for an antipasto salad.

# French Red Onion Soup (serves 4)

*Ingredients*
450ml/15fl oz of chicken broth
450ml/15fl oz of water
2 whole star anise
6 black peppercorns
1kg/35oz of red onions, cut into 1/2-inch wedges
3 tablespoons of olive oil
115ml/4fl oz of dry red wine
4 (1-inch-thick) slices of baguette
200g/7oz of coarsely grated Manchego or Gruyère

*Preparation*
Bring broth, water, spices, and 1/2 teaspoon of salt to a boil.
Remove from heat and allow to rest for 15 minutes.

Meanwhile, cook the onions in the olive
oil with 1/4 teaspoon salt in a heavy
medium pot over medium heat,
covered, stirring occasionally until
deep golden (about 15 minutes).
Add wine and boil, uncovered,
until reduced to 2 tablespoons
(about 1 minute).

Strain broth through a sieve into onion
mixture and briskly simmer, uncovered for
10 minutes. Season with salt.

*Pre-heating*
Ladle the soup into 4 oven-proof bowls
set in a 4-sided sheet pan. Place baguette
slices on top and sprinkle with cheese. Grill
about 6 inches from the heat until cheese is
melted and bubbling.

# Tomato & Brown Lentil Soup (serves 4)

*Ingredients*
1 large onion
225g/8oz of brown lentils
55ml/2fl oz of extra virgin olive oil
1 clove of garlic
55g/2oz of tomato paste
2 small dried chillies
1 bay leaf
1L/34fl oz of water
salt and freshly ground black pepper to taste

*Preparation*
Finely chop the onion. Rinse lentils in cold water; drain well. Heat the olive oil in a large heavy-based pan. Add the onion and garlic and stir over a low heat for 10 minutes.

Add the tomato paste, chillies, bay leaf, lentils and water and bring to the boil. Reduce the heat, simmer, covered for 30 minutes or until the lentils are soft. Remove chillies and bay leaf and discard. Add pepper to taste.

Serve with crusty bread, garnished with fresh red and green chillies.

This dish can be made up to two days ahead. Store covered in the refrigerator and reheat just before serving.

# Tortellini, Tomato & Spinach Soup (serves 4)

*Ingredients*
1 tablespoon of olive oil
115g/4oz of minced onion (about 1/2 small onion)
1 garlic clove, minced
1250ml/35fl oz of chicken broth or vegetable broth
400g/14oz can of whole tomatoes, coarsely chopped
250g/9oz packet of fresh tortellini or dried tortellini
salt and cracked black pepper to taste
300g/11oz of fresh spinach or frozen spinach, defrosted and chopped
55g/2oz of freshly grated Parmesan cheese (optional)

*Preparation*

In a soup pot, heat the olive oil over a medium high heat.
Sauté the onion and garlic, stirring often until onions are translucent, about 5 to 7 minutes.

Add the broth and tomatoes, turn heat up to high, and bring to the boil.
Add the tortellini and cook according to packet instructions. When the tortellini is almost done, add the spinach and taste, adjusting seasonings with salt and pepper.

Serve immediately.

Garnish each serving with a sprinkling of Parmesan.

# Eggs With Serrano Ham & Manchego Cheese, Green Olive Relish & Migas (serves 4)

*Ingredients*

Relish:
55g/2oz of chopped pitted brine-cured green olives
55g/2oz of chopped drained roasted red bell pepper from jar
1 tablespoon of extra-virgin olive oil
1 teaspoon of chopped fresh oregano

Migas:
2 tablespoons of extra-virgin olive oil
2 small garlic cloves, pressed
4 3/4 inch thick slices of pain rustique or ciabatta, cut into 3/4-inch cubes
(about 4 generous cups)

Salad:
1 tablespoon of extra-virgin olive oil
1 tablespoon of Sherry wine vinegar
55g/2oz of finely chopped shallots
115g/4oz of (lightly packed) arugula leaves
115g/4oz of (lightly packed) torn baby frisée
Fleur de sel or coarse kosher salt

Eggs:
1 tablespoon of extra-virgin olive oil
4 large eggs
115g/4oz very thinly sliced Manchego cheese
4 very thin slices Serrano ham or prosciutto

*Preparation*

For relish:
Combine all ingredients in small bowl. The relish can be made one day ahead. Cover and refrigerate.

**For migas:**
Preheat oven to 190°C. Stir the olive oil and garlic in a large bowl. Add the bread cubes and toss to coat well. Transfer the bread into a heavy large baking sheet and bake until lightly toasted yet still chewy, about 10 minutes. Allow to cool.

**For salad:**
Whisk the olive oil, vinegar and shallots in large bowl. Add the arugula, frisée, and migas; toss well. Season lightly with fleur de sel. Divide the salad among 4 plates.

**For eggs:**
Heat olive oil in large non-stick pan over a medium heat. Add the eggs; immediately cover the top of each egg with cheese, dividing evenly. Cover and cook until egg whites are just set and cheese softens, about 2 minutes. Carefully transfer one egg onto each plate; top with ham and season with pepper. Top each egg with relish, dividing evenly.

# Asparagus Wrapped In Serrano Ham (serves 4)

*Ingredients*
3 tablespoons of extra-virgin olive oil
2 tablespoons of sherry vinegar
1 shallot, minced
1/4 teaspoon of salt
1/8 teaspoon of freshly ground black pepper
12 stalks each of white and green asparagus, ends trimmed (24 total)
6 thin slices of serrano ham (or prosciutto), each cut into 4 strips
30g/1oz of frisée
30g/1oz of mixed greens
220g/7oz each of seedless green and red grapes, halved
55g/2oz of sliced roasted almonds

Whisk the olive oil, vinegar, shallot, salt and pepper in a bowl. Set aside. Cook the asparagus in simmering water until soft but still crisp, 3 to 4 minutes. Rinse under cold water and drain. Wrap a strip of ham around each asparagus stalk. Toss the frisée, greens and grapes with dressing in a bowl, then transfer to a platter; top with asparagus. Garnish with almonds.

## Chargrilled Peppers With Anchovies (serves 4)

*Ingredients*

4 tablespoons of extra virgin olive oil
4 sweet red bell peppers
4 sweet yellow bell peppers
1 can of anchovies in olive oil
2 tablespoons black olives
1 bunch of marjoram or flat leafed parsley
salt and freshly ground black pepper to taste

*Preparation*

Place the peppers on a gas grill and char them all over. When suitably blackened place them in a plastic bag and seal it.
The residual heat will complete the cooking process.

Once the peppers have cooled remove the bag and rub away the skin.

Halve and discard the seeds and cores.

Sprinkle with the anchovies and black olives. Dress with olive oil herbs and season with salt and pepper.

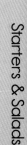

# Balsamic Roast Tomatoes (serves 4)

*Ingredients*
6 tomatoes
balsamic vinegar
1 large or 2 small cloves of garlic
olive oil
fresh thyme

*Preparation*
Preheat the oven to 180°C. Cut the tomatoes in half horizontally (around the equator) and pop them in the roasting dish, cut side up. Slice the garlic thinly and push the slices into the tomato pulp.

Splash over some balsamic vinegar and olive oil, shake the roasting tin so they're all covered, and then sprinkle over the thyme and some salt and pepper, just enough to get a bit on each tomato half. Put it in the oven for about 30 minutes, keeping an eye on it to make sure it's not browning too quickly.

# Pasta with Garlic & Olive Oil (serves 4-6)

*Ingredients*
500g/18oz of pasta
salt
115ml/4fl oz of extra virgin olive oil
4-6 garlic cloves, peeled & chopped
60g/2oz of chopped fresh parsley
freshly ground pepper

*Preparation*
Peel and chop the garlic and parsley. While the pasta is cooking, heat the olive oil and garlic over medium heat in a saucepan until the garlic begins to turn pale gold. Remove the pan from the heat and add 3/4 of the parsley, salt & pepper to taste. Drain the pasta and combine with the sauce in a separate bowl and toss until all the spaghetti is coated.

# Salads

## Fennel, Olive & Blood Orange Salad (serves 2)

*Ingredients*
3 fennel bulbs
60g/2oz of mesclun salad mix
2 oranges, segmented
1 orange for juice
75g/2 1/2oz of pitted olives
30g/1oz Italian parsley leaves
75ml/2 1/2fl oz of extra virgin olive oil
1 lemon, juiced
100g/3 1/2oz of parmesan cheese
salt and pepper

*Preparation*
Get a good grasp on your fennel, and trim off the tips and any bruised sections. Slice very thinly.
Add orange juice, olive oil, salt and pepper together in a small bowl and whisk until they are well mixed, making a vinaigrette dressing.

Combine the other ingredients into a large salad serving bowl, and pour the vinaigrette of the top. Gently toss for several seconds. Shave the parmesan over the top and serve when ready.

## Asian Pear & Frisée Salad (serves 2)

*Ingredients*
55ml/2fl oz of extra-virgin olive oil
115ml/5fl oz of balsamic vinegar
1 teaspoon of packed brown sugar
2 medium leeks (white and pale green parts only), halved lengthwise and thinly sliced
220g/8oz of frisée, torn (8 cups)
1 large Asian pear (220-280g/8-10oz), thinly sliced

Boil the vinegar with sugar and 1/4 teaspoon salt in a small heavy saucepan, stirring, until reduced by half. Transfer into a cup.

Wash off the leeks and pat dry. Cook in olive oil with 1/4 teaspoon of salt in a saucepan over a medium heat, stirring occasionally, until softened.

Arrange frisée and pear on plates. Drizzle with hot leeks in oil, then vinegar reduction. Grind pepper over salads.

## Ravioli Salad With Vegetables & Ham (serves 4-6)

*Ingredients*
55ml/2fl oz of olive oil
55ml/2fl oz of red wine vinegar
1 tablespoon of chopped fresh rosemary or 1 1/2 teaspoons dried
1 large garlic clove, minced
1 teaspoon of sugar
1/2 teaspoon of dried crushed red pepper
500g/18oz packet of fresh cheese ravioli, fresh cooked
340g/12oz of diced ham
1 red bell pepper, diced
100g/3 1/2oz jar of marinated mushrooms, drained
4 green onions, chopped
black olives (optional)
grated Parmesan cheese

*Preparation*
Combine the first 6 ingredients in a large bowl and whisk to blend. Rinse the ravioli under cold water to cool; drain. Add the ravioli, ham, bell pepper, mushrooms and green onions to vinaigrette; toss to coat.

Season the salad to taste with salt and pepper. Cover and chill for at least 30 minutes. Arrange salad on large platter. Garnish with olives, if desired. Serve, passing Parmesan cheese separately.

# Caesar Salad (serves 2)

*Ingredients: For the salad*
Olive oil for frying
1 large cos /romaine lettuce washed and torn into strips
2 slices of bread, crust removed and cut into croutons

*Ingredients: For the dressing*
1 large free range egg, at room temperature
1 garlic clove peeled
3 anchovy fillets
2 tablespoons of lemon juice
1 tablespoon of Worcestershire sauce
3 tablespoons of olive oil
30g/1oz of Parmesan cheese, grated
course sea salt and black pepper

*Preparation: Dressing*
Place the egg in a pan of boiling water.
cook for one minute,
then plunge into
cold water and
reserve. When
cool, crack the egg
into the bowl of a food
processor. Add the garlic,
anchovies, lemon juice and
Worcestershire sauce. Blend well,
while slowly pouring in the olive oil.
Blend in the grated parmesan. Season to
taste.

*Preparation: Salad*
Toast the croutons in a frying pan with the olive oil. Add the lettuce to a
serving bowl, pour the dressing over it and mix well. Scatter with croutons.

# Hot Mediterranean Chicken Salad (serves 6)

*Ingredients*
6 boneless, skinless chicken breast halves
115ml/4fl oz of olive oil
1 medium onion, sliced
1 clove garlic, crushed
1 tablespoon of chopped fresh oregano or 1 1/2 tablespoons dried
170g/6oz of Greek or Nicoise olives
225g/8oz of cooked small green beans
225g/8oz of halved cherry tomatoes
2 tablespoons of lemon zest
1 to 2 tablespoons of wine vinegar
juice of 1 lemon
salt and pepper, to taste
300g/10oz finely shredded lettuce
lemon wedges

*Preparation*
Season the chicken breasts
with salt and pepper and
sauté in a little of the olive oil
over medium heat until just
done, about 5 minutes a side.
Do not overcook. Cool, and pull
the meat into bite-size pieces. Set
aside.

Add onion to additional olive oil and sauté until
softened. Add garlic and oregano and cook one more
minute. Add olives, cooked beans, tomatoes and lemon zest and stir until
heated through. Add reserved chicken and season to taste with vinegar,
lemon juice, salt and pepper.

To serve, season lettuce with remaining olive oil, salt, pepper and a bit of
lemon juice. Divide equally on 6 plates. Spoon hot chicken salad onto lettuce
and serve.

# Chorizo Salad (serves 2)

*Ingredients: Salad*
2 tablespoons of olive oil
half a large chorizo (about 225g/8oz), sliced
mixed salad leaves
1/2 a sweet red bell pepper, seeded and sliced into thin strips
4 spring onions (scallion), diced
cooked new potatoes, halved, optional
2 free range hard boiled eggs
a handful of chopped flat leaf parsley
course sea salt and freshly grounded black pepper

*Ingredients: Dressing*
3 tablespoons of olive oil
1 tablespoon of red wine vinegar
dash of course grained mustard

*Preparation: Dressing*
To make the dressing, whisk together the olive oil and vinegar and add a dash of course grained french mustard.

*Preparation: Salad*
Heat the olive oil and fry the chorizo until lightly browned. Arrange the salad leaves, pepper, spring onions and potatoes on 2 dinner plates or in 2 pasta bowls. Sprinkle with the chorizo.

Shell and quarter the eggs, and then carefully place on top of the chorizo salad. Pour the dressing over the salad, season and sprinkle with the parsley.

## Beetroot & Feta Salad (serves 2)

*Ingredients*
6 - 8 beetroots
200g/8oz of feta cheese
a handful of chopped mint
115ml/4fl oz of olive oil
4 tablespoons of balsamic vinegar
course sea salt and black pepper

*Preparation*
Slice the beetroot in thick slices
and divide them between the
serving plates.

Sprinkle with the feta and mint and
season to taste. Sprinkle the oil and
the vinegar over the dishes and
serve.

## Greek Salad (serves 2)

*Ingredients*
Romaine lettuce leaves
170ml/6fl oz of extra virgin olive oil
55ml/2fl oz of good quality red wine vinegar
1 1/2 teaspoons of crushed oregano
1 teaspoon of salt
a pinch of pepper

*Preparation*
Tear up the lettuce leaves and arrange on a plate. Whisk together the
remaining ingredients in a bowl, or place in a tightly covered jar and shake
to combine. The dressing will turn a light colour with a creamy texture as the
oil and vinegar combine.

Mains & Desserts

# Mains

## Kale & Olive Oil Mashed Potato (serves 4-6)

For this recipe, be sure to wash the kale well (or spinach, or chard) - dirt and grit hides in the leaves. If you stir the kale in too much it can lend a slight green cast to your potatoes, so briefly stir it in just before serving.

*Ingredients*
1 1/2kg/37oz of potatoes, peeled and cut into large chunks
sea salt
4 tablespoons of extra virgin olive oil
4 cloves of garlic, minced
1 bunch of kale, large stems stripped and discarded, leaves chopped
115ml/4fl oz of warm milk or cream
freshly ground black pepper
5 scallions, white and tender green parts, chopped
55g/2oz freshly grated Parmesan, for garnish
fried shallots, for garnish (optional)

*Preparation*
Put the potatoes in a large pot and cover with water. Add a pinch of salt. Bring the water to a boil and continue boiling for 20 minutes, or until the potatoes are tender.

Heat two tablespoons of olive oil in a large pan or skillet over a medium-high heat. Add the garlic, chopped kale, a big pinch of salt, and sauté just until tender - about a minute. Set aside.

Mash the potatoes with a potato masher or fork. Slowly stir in the milk a few big splashes at a time. You are after a thick, creamy texture, so if your potatoes are on the dry side keep adding milk until the texture is right. Season with salt and pepper. Dump the kale on top of the potatoes and give them a quick stir. Transfer into a serving bowl, make a well in the center of the potatoes and pour the remaining olive oil. Sprinkle with the scallions, Parmesan cheese and shallots.

# Pasta With Lemon Olive Oil (serves 4-6)

*Ingredients*
zest of 1 lemon
75ml/2 1/2fl oz of lemon juice
115ml/4fl oz of extra virgin olive oil
1-2 large garlic cloves minced
115g/4oz of black or green olives, pitted and sliced
2 tablespoons of fresh chopped thyme or basil
salt and freshly coarse ground black pepper
500g/18oz of pasta

*Preparation*
You can use a lemon olive oil or add the
lemon: Zest or grate the lemon and
combine with the lemon juice, olive
oil, garlic cloves, olives, thyme, and
the salt, and pepper in a large
serving bowl.

Toss the hot cooked pasta
with the sauce.

# Pizza Dough For Thin Crust Pizza (makes two 12inch pizzas)

*Ingredients*

550g/20oz of all-purpose flour (may substitute whole wheat flour for 1 cup of the all-purpose)
1 packet of active dry yeast
1/4 teaspoon of salt
225ml/7 1/2fl oz of warm water
1/2-1 tablespoon of olive oil
cornmeal, for sprinkling

*Preparation*

Mix a little sugar into the warm water.
Sprinkle the yeast on top. Wait for 10 minutes
or until it gets all foamy. Pour into a large bowl.
Add flour, salt, olive oil.

Combine. Knead for 6-8 minutes until you have a moderately stiff dough that is smooth and elastic (add a bit more flour if you need to).

Cover and let rest for 20-30 minutes.

Lightly grease two 12-inch pizza pans. Sprinkle with a little bit of cornmeal.

Divide dough in half. Place each half on a pizza pan and pat it with your fingers until it stretches over the whole pan. Try to make it thicker around the edge.

If desired, pre-bake at 220°C for 10 minutes. Then spread with pizza sauce and use the toppings of your choice. Bake at 220°C for 10-20 minutes longer or until bubbly and hot.

If you don't want to use all the dough, you can freeze it. Take a portion of dough, form into a ball, rub olive oil over it and place it in a freezer bag (the oil makes it easier to take out of the bag). When you want to make a pizza, take dough out of freezer and allow to thaw before using.

## Roasted Garlic Mashed Potatoes (serves 4-6)

*Ingredients*
1kg/35oz of potatoes
1 head of garlic
1 tablespoon of olive oil
55ml/2fl oz of sour cream
4 tablespoons of butter
milk or cream, as required
salt
white pepper

*Ingredients*
Separate the head of the garlic into individual cloves. Toss in olive oil and wrap tightly in small piece of aluminum foil. Bake at 180°C for 45 minutes.

When the garlic has cooled to the touch you should be able to squeeze it out of the 'paper' shell of the individual cloves. Mash the roasted garlic with a fork, or force through a fine strainer.

If you use a ricer as recommended below, simply rice the garlic along with the potatoes. Peel and boil potatoes in salted water until tender. Force the cooked potatoes through a ricer (recommended) or mash by your usual method.

Put the riced potatoes, garlic, sour cream, butter, and salt and white pepper in a mixer bowl, and whip at medium speed until smooth.

Add cream or milk to adjust consistency.

# Spaghetti With Tuna Capers & Chilli (serves 4-6)

*Ingredients*
1/2 red onion finely chopped
1 finely chopped chilli
1 clove of crushed garlic
1 tablespoon of rinsed capers
a small bunch of roughly chopped parsley
1/2 juiced lemon
olive oil
1 tin of drained tuna in spring water
500g/18oz of pasta

*Preparation*
Cook the spaghetti as per the instructions on pack. Mix together the rest of the ingredients with 2 to 3 tablespoons of extra virgin oil in a large bowl.

Drain the cooked pasta and toss the hot spaghetti through the mixture, season and serve.

# Roasted Squash & Ricotta Penne (serves 4)

*Ingredients*
750g/26oz of cubed butternut squash
2 sprigs of chopped rosemary
2 finely chopped red chillies
4 tablespoons of olive oil
200g/7oz of ricotta cheese
300g/10 1/2oz of penne pasta

*Preparation*
Heat the oven to 200°C and roast the squash, herbs and chillies for about 20 minutes until tender. Cook the penne as per pack instructions.

Toss the squash mixture through the drained penne and serve with dots of ricotta.

# Spiced Prawn & Mango Noodles (serves 4)

*Ingredients*

100g/3 1/2oz of fine thread egg noodles
1 pack of prawns
1 finely chopped chilli
1 crushed garlic clove
1 handful of coriander leaves
3 tablespoons of olive oil
1 sliced mango
sea salt and black pepper

*Preparation*

Cook the noodles as per the instructions on the pack.

Stir fry the prawns in a little olive oil and add the finely chopped chillies and garlic.

Drain the noodles and toss through the stir fry mixture. Serve into big bowl and add the slices of mango.

Finish off with a sprinkle of coriander leaves. Season to taste.

# Desserts

## Olive Oil Vanilla Ice Cream (serves 4-6)

*Ingredients*
8 egg yolks
225g/8oz of sugar
pinch salt
225ml/8fl oz of milk
675ml/23fl oz of heavy cream
1/3 of a vanilla bean, split and scraped
6 tablespoons of extra virgin olive oil
2 teaspoons of sea salt

*Preparation*
Combine the cream, milk, sugar, egg yolks and vanilla bean in a medium sized sauce pan. Bring it up to the boil, then sift the mixture through a medium strainer and chill. Process according to your ice cream maker instructions.

When serving the ice cream, drizzle with 1-1/2 tablespoons of olive oil and sprinkle with sea salt.

# Extra Rich Brownies (serves 4-6)

*Ingredients*
220g/8oz of bittersweet chocolate
10 tablespoons of olive oil
4 eggs
170g/6oz of ground almonds
225g/8oz of granulated sugar
1 teaspoon of baking soda
115g/4oz of all purpose flour

*Preparation*
Preheat the oven to 180°C. Grease an 8x10-inch rectangular baking pan.

Coarsely chop the walnuts. Break the chocolate into pieces and melt in a glass bowl over a pan of boiling water. Add the butter or olive oil and stir to blend. Remove from the heat. Set aside.

In another bowl, combine the eggs, ground almonds, and sugar. Add to the melted chocolate and stir to blend.

In another bowl, combine the baking soda and flour. Sift into the chocolate mixture. Stir to blend. Add the walnuts and stir again.

Transfer the batter to the prepared pan and bake for 20-25 minutes. Remove the pan from the oven. Leave to stand for 5 minutes, then unmold onto a cooling rack and cool completely. Cut into squares for serving. These are best served cold.

# Lemon Olive Oil Crème Brûlée (serves 4-6)

*Ingredients*
300ml/10fl oz of double cream
10 egg yolks
2 whole eggs
1 drop of vanilla essence
350g/12oz granulated sugar
1 sprig of rosemary
zest of 2 lemons
225ml/7 1/2fl oz of lemon olive oil

*Preparation*
Combine cream, rosemary, sugar, vanilla, zests of lemons, and olive oil in a pan. Heat to just below boiling point. Do no boil, or the cream will break and you'll have to start over again. Remove from heat, and remove rosemary over about 5 minutes.

Whisk the egg yolks, and let them come up to room temperature. Heat the cream mixture again, taking care not to boil, and add half of this mixture to your egg yolks. Whisk together, and then add the mixture back into the pan with the rest of the cream mixture. Stir over low heat until the mixture begins to thicken.

Remove from heat and place on a bowl of ice cubes. Stir and allow mixture to rest for 2 minutes.

Fill ramekins with crème brûlée mixture, and place on a bain-marie. Place bain-marie in a 180°C oven, and add enough water to the pan to come half way up the ramekins. Cover with a sheet pan, and bake until custards set. Cool at room temperature, and then put in refrigerator.

When cool, sprinkle sugar on top to make a crust, and burn with a torch until very deeply caramelised.

# Golden Banana Cake (serves 4-6)

*Ingredients*

145g/5oz of all-purpose flour
1/8 teaspoon of baking powder
pinch of baking soda
8 tablespoons of unsalted butter, softened
1 1/2 tablespoons of olive oil
170g/6oz of sugar
4 large eggs
1 extra ripe medium sized banana, peeled and mashed

*Preparation*

Preheat the oven to 160°C. Butter an 8 1/2 x 4 1/2 x 2 1/2-inch loaf pan. Dust the pan with flour, tapping out the excess. Sift together the flour, baking powder, and baking soda.

In the bowl of an electric mixer fitted with the paddle attachment, mix together the butter, olive oil and sugar at low speed. Increase the speed to a medium setting, and add the eggs one at a time, beating well after each addition.

Mix in the mashed banana. Add the flour mixture and mix just until combined.

Scrape the batter into the prepared pan, smoothing the top with a spatula.

Bake the cake for 55 to 60 minutes, until the top is golden brown and a toothpick inserted in the centre of the cake comes out clean. Cool the cake in the pan on a wire rack for 15 minutes.

Unmold the cake and cool completely on the rack. Store in an airtight container at room temperature for 3 days, 1 week refrigerated, or 2 months frozen.

# Sweet Olive Oil Quick Bread (serves 6-8)

*Ingredients*
650g/23oz of unbleached all-purpose flour
2 teaspoons of baking powder
a pinch salt
1 cup of sugar
2 eggs, lightly beaten
170ml/6fl oz of milk
115ml/4fl oz of extra virgin olive oil
115g/4oz of raisins
grated zest of 1 lemon
unsalted butter for loaf pan
55g/2oz of pine nuts

*Preparation*
Preheat oven to 180°C. In a mixing bowl, stir together the flour, baking powder and salt. Stir in the sugar. Add the eggs, milk and olive oil, and beat well.

Toss the raisins in a little flour to coat them lightly. Add the raisins and lemon zest to the flour and egg mixture and stir to distribute evenly.

Butter and flour a loaf pan. Transfer the batter into the pan and smooth the surface. Sprinkle the top with pine nuts.

Bake for 55 minutes, or until a thin skewer inserted in the centre comes out dry. Let cool for a few minutes.

Unmold and cool on a rack.

# Walnut Orange Cake (serves 6-8)

*Ingredients*
non-stick olive oil spray
350g/12oz cups of chopped walnuts
225g/8oz of all purpose flour
1 tablespoon of baking powder
4 large eggs
350g/12oz of sugar
115ml/4fl oz of fresh orange juice
1 tablespoon of finely grated orange peel
115ml/4fl oz of olive oil
powdered sugar

*Preparation*
Preheat oven to 180°C. Spray a 9 inch diameter springform tin with non-stick olive oil spray. Place parchment paper in the bottom of the tin and spray paper.
Grind walnuts in processor until finely ground but not powdery. Combine ground walnuts, flour, and baking powder in medium bowl; set aside.

Using an electric mixer, beat eggs in large bowl until frothy, about 2 minutes. Gradually add sugar, beating until light, thick, and pale yellow, about 4 minutes. Gradually add walnut-flour mixture; then add orange juice, orange peel, and olive oil, beating just until blended. Transfer batter to prepared pan.

Place pan on rimmed baking sheet, and bake cake until tester inserted into center comes out clean, about 1 hour. Cool cake completely in pan on rack.

Release pan sides. Carefully invert cake onto platter and remove parchment paper. Sprinkle powdered sugar on top of the cake and serve.

Sauces, Dips
& Dressings

# Sauces

## Anchovy Sauce

*Ingredients*
2 cans (60g/2oz) of anchovies in olive oil, drained
2 cloves of garlic
2 sprigs of fresh thyme (or 1/4 teaspoon dried)
1-1/2 tablespoons of Dijon mustard
3 tablespoons of red wine vinegar
freshly ground black pepper
450ml/15fl oz of virgin olive oil

*Preparation*
Combine the anchovies, garlic, thyme, Dijon mustard, red wine vinegar and pepper in a blender or food processor and puree for about one minute.

With the machine running, add the olive oil in a thin stream and process until the mixture is thick and smooth.

This sauce for salads or hard-boiled eggs can be kept for several weeks in the refrigerator.

# Olive Oil Hollandaise Sauce

*Ingredients*
1 tablespoon of white wine vinegar
1 teaspoon of white peppercorns, crushed
3 egg yolks
250g/9oz of olive oil, warmed slightly
sea salt
cayenne pepper
1 tablespoon of lemon juice

*Preparation*
When whisking and cooking an egg-yolk mixture in recipes such as hollandaise sauce, check to make sure it's cooked by lifting the whisk from the mixture. If the ribbon of yolk trailed from the whisk remains visible on the sauce surface, it's ready. If it disappears immediately, it requires more cooking and whisking. If you don't cook it enough at this stage, the taste of raw egg yolk remains.

Put vinegar and white pepper in small saucepan and reduce by two-thirds. Place a bowl over a saucepan of very hot (but not boiling) water. Add the egg yolks, vinegar mix and 1 tablespoon of warm water. Whisk the mixture until it's creamy and light.

Slowly whisk in the olive oil, a little at a time. If the mixture gets sticky, add a little warm water. Continue whisking, adding the remaining oil.

Season with salt, cayenne and lemon juice.

Serve immediately.

# Tomato Coulis

Serve this sauce as an accompaniment to steamed seafood such as sole, shrimp or lobster.

*Ingredients: Tomato Coulis*
700g/25oz of under-ripe tomatoes, peeled and seeded
3 tablespoons of extra-virgin olive oil
salt, to taste

*Ingredients: Garlic Sauce*
2 garlic cloves
bread crumbs from 1 bread roll
1 anchovy, washed
1 small bunch of parsley, washed
salt and freshly ground black pepper
4 tablespoons of extra-virgin olive oil
4 tablespoons of vinegar

*Preparation: Tomato Coulis*
Combine the ingredients in a blender or a food processor until smooth.

*Preparation: Garlic Sauce*
This sauce is usually used for boiled fish and meat.
Soak the bread crumbs in a small bowl of water and vinegar for 5 minutes; remove and squeeze the juices out.

Place in a blender, add the parsley, garlic, anchovy, and a pinch of salt and pepper. Add the olive oil and blend for 5 minutes.

Makes about 1 cup.

# Superb Spaghetti Sauce

*Ingredients*
700g/25oz of ground beef
2 tablespoons of olive oil
1 medium onion, chopped
2 cloves of garlic, minced (to taste)
2 bay leaves
1 teaspoon of oregano
1 teaspoon of dried basil
1 teaspoon of Italian seasoning
1 teaspoon of salt (or to taste)
ground pepper
170g/6oz of tomato puree
450g/16oz of tomato sauce
800g/28oz of diced tomatoes
200g/8oz of fresh mushrooms, sliced and sautéed in butter (optional)
parmesan cheese, freshly grated (optional)

*Preparation*
Brown the ground beef, onion and garlic in olive oil with the bay leaves, oregano, basil, Italian seasoning, salt and pepper.

Add the tomato paste, tomato sauce and diced tomatoes. Stir well and bring to a simmer over a medium heat. Cover and simmer for 1 1/2 hours.

Use sauce to top your cooked spaghetti. Top with sauteed mushroom and parmesan as required.

# Marinade For Lamb & Pork

*Ingredients*
2 tablespoons of smoked paprika
1 handful of crushed fresh thyme
4 garlic cloves
8 tablespoons of olive oil
2 tablespoons of sherry vinegar
salt and pepper

*Preparation*
Combine the ingredients
with a pestle and mortar until
smooth.

# Finger-Lickin BBQ Sauce

*Ingredients*
1/2 white onion
3 cloves of garlic
3 tablespoons of olive oil
375ml/13fl oz of ketchup
115ml/4fl oz of white vinegar
75ml/2.5fl oz of brown sugar
75ml/2.5fl oz of Worcestershire sauce
2 teaspoons of chilli powder
1/4 teaspoon of cayenne pepper

*Preparation*
Put the olive oil in a saucepan on a medium heat and cook the onion and garlic until they are soft.

Then add the white vinegar, ketchup, brown sugar, Worcestershire sauce, chilli powder, and cayenne pepper.

Allow to simmer for 30 minutes.

Sauces, Dips & Dressings

# Walnut Pesto

A great sauce to top pasta, but can also be spread over goat's cheese on a crouton as an easy hors d'oeuvre.

*Ingredients*
225ml/7 1/2fl oz of walnuts, toasted
2 cloves of garlic, cleaned
1 handful of fresh basil
1 handful fresh of flat-leaf parsley
1 pinch of dried chilli flakes
75ml/2.5fl oz of extra virgin olive oil
juice of one lemon
salt and pepper

*Preparation*
Place all the ingredients except for the oil and lemon in the bowl of a food processor. Pulse several times until ingredients are crumbly.

Add the oil in a steady stream and then the lemon juice. Taste and adjust seasoning.

Will keep for several days in the refrigerator.

# Dips

## Alioli

*Ingredients*
2 or 3 fresh garlic cloves, peeled and chopped
large pinch of coarse sea salt or Kosher salt
1 egg yolk, at room temperature
juice of half a lemon
150ml/5fl oz of pure olive oil (not extra virgin)
75ml/2.5fl oz of extra virgin olive oil
freshly ground black pepper

*Preparation*
Place the garlic and salt in a food processor fitted with a metal blade, or in a blender. Pulse for 2 seconds. Add the egg yolk and lemon juice, and pulse on and off until blended. Turn on and begin adding the olive oil (pure first, then extra virgin) in a thin stream.

If it becomes too thick, thin it out with some room-temperature water and continue adding oil until you've used it all. Finish with pepper and (if necessary) a bit more salt.

The reason for using 2/3 pure olive oil is to keep the flavour of the oil from becoming overpowering.

## Parsley Dip

*Ingredients*
1 large bunch of parsley (only the leaves)
1 slice bread (2cm thick)
1 small onion
1 clove of garlic
2 tablespoons of olive oil
300g/10 1/2oz of strained yoghurt
juice of 1 lemon
salt and pepper

*Preparation*
Soak the bread in water, strain and place in a blender with the parsley, onion, garlic, salt and pepper. Blend the mixture and then add the yoghurt, olive oil and lemon juice. Garnish with parsley leaves and olives.

Can be eaten as an appetizer or with vegetables, boiled eggs or fish.

## Yoghurt Dip With Parsley

*Ingredients*
300g/10 1/2oz of strained yoghurt
2 tablespoons of dried parsley
1 small grated onion
2 tablespoons of olive oil
1 tablespoon of lemon juice
salt and pepper

*Preparation*
Mix the yoghurt with the onion, parsley, salt and pepper. Continue to stir adding the olive oil and lemon juice until well mixed. Store in the fridge.

# Yoghurt Dip With Mint

*Ingredients*
300g/10 1/2oz of strained yoghurt
1 tablespoon of dried mint
2 tablespoons of olive oil
1 tablespoon lemon juice
salt and pepper

*Preparation*
Mix the yoghurt with the mint, salt and pepper. Continue to stir adding the olive oil and lemon juice until well mixed. Store in the fridge.

Can be eaten as an appetizer or with fresh fish.

# Yoghurt Dip With Dill

*Ingredients*
300g/10 1/2oz of strained yoghurt
1 tablespoon of dried dill
1 mashed clove garlic
2 tablespoons of olive oil
1 tablespoon of lemon juice
salt and pepper

*Preparation*
Mix the yoghurt with the garlic, dill, salt and pepper. Continue to stir adding the olive oil and lemon juice until well mixed. Store in the fridge.

Can be eaten as an appetizer or with vegetables and green salads.

# Yoghurt & Carrot Dip

*Ingredients*
500g/17 1/2oz of carrots
300g/10 1/2oz of strained yoghurt
2 cloves of mashed garlic
3-4 tablespoons of olive oil
1 tablespoon of lemon juice
115g/4oz of ground walnuts (optional)
salt

*Preparation*
Scrape the carrots and grate them. Whip the yoghurt with remaining ingredients, add the carrots and mix well.

Can be eaten as an appetizer or starter.

# Yoghurt & Courgette Dip

*Ingredients*
500g/17 1/2oz of courgettes
300g/10 1/2oz of strained yoghurt
2 cloves of mashed garlic
3-4 tablespoons of olive oil
1 tablespoon of lemon juice
2 tablespoons of finely chopped dill or mint
5-6 black olives
salt and pepper

*Preparation*
Wash and cut the courgettes in pieces. Boil in salted water until tender and drain well. Put them in a bowl and mash completely with a fork.

Add the yoghurt, garlic, dill or mint, olive oil, lemon juice, salt and pepper and mix well. Garnish with olives. Can be eaten as an appetizer or starter.

# Houmous

*Ingredients*
200g/7oz of chickpeas
2 cloves of garlic
3 tablespoons of olive oil
3 tablespoons of tahini (ground sesame seeds)
4 tablespoons of lemon juice
3 tablespoons of water
1 teaspoon of paprika (optional)
salt and pepper
parsley

*Preparation*
Soak the chick peas the night before in a large bowl with water. The next day boil them until soft. Drain and allow to cool.

In a bowl dilute tahini with water. Put the chick peas into a mixer and, grinding constantly, add the salt, pepper, tahini, garlic, olive oil and lemon juice until the houmous becomes smooth and creamy.

Serve cold, sprinkled with paprika and garnished with parsley.

Can be eaten as an appetizer or as a starter.

# Tzatziki

*Ingredients*
470ml/16fl oz of sour cream (or Greek-style super thick yoghurt)
1 cucumber, peeled, grated on a box grater, salted lightly for 5 minutes and squeezed between the hands to remove the water
3 garlic cloves, mashed to a paste
115ml/4fl oz of olive oil
1 tablespoon of red wine vinegar
1 tablespoon of minced fresh dill (optional)
salt

*Preparation*

Just mix everything up together until it is all blended and the oil has emulsified into the yoghurt/sour cream. Taste for seasoning, and add salt if you think necessary. Put in a re-sealable container.

Allow to rest in the refrigerator for at least 2-3 hours before using to allow the flavours to come out.

Use as a salad dressing or a dip for crudites.

## Avocado Dip

*Ingredients*
2 avocados
1 small grated onion
2 tablespoons of finely chopped parsley
2 tablespoons of lemon juice
2 tablespoons of olive oil
salt and pepper

*Preparation*
Peel the avocados, remove the stones and then mash in a deep bowl. Add the other ingredients and whisk until creamy.

Garnish with parsley and keep it in the fridge.

This can be used on its own to dip small vegetable pieces or on meat, fish and salads.

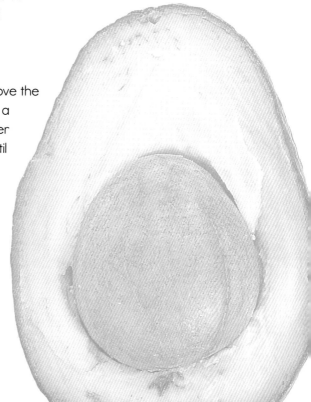

# Dressings

## Italian Herb Infused Olive Oil

*Ingredients*
6 fresh basil leaves
2 sprigs of fresh thyme
2 sprigs of fresh rosemary
2 sprigs of fresh oregano
355ml/12fl oz of extra virgin olive oil

*Preparation*
Place the basil, thyme,
rosemary and oregano in
a 350m/12fl oz bottle.

Using a funnel, pour
the oil into the bottle.

Cover tightly, and refrigerate unused portions. Use within 2 to 3 days.

## Balsamic Vinegar & Olive Oil Dressing

*Ingredients*
1 sprig of fresh oregano
1 sprig of fresh thyme
235ml/8fl oz of olive oil
60ml/2fl oz of balsamic vinegar
salt and pepper to taste

*Preparation*
In a medium glass mixing bowl combine the oregano, thyme, oil, vinegar, salt
and pepper. Mix together and pour mixture into a bottle, using a funnel to
keep yourself from losing oil. Cover tightly and store at room temperature.

## Lemon Vinaigrette

*Ingredients*
2 1/2 teaspoon of lemon juice
1/2 teaspoon of lemon peel, grated
1 teaspoon of sherry vinegar
1 clove of garlic, minced
3 tablespoons of olive oil
a pinch of salt

*Preparation*
In a small bowl, mix together the lemon juice, lemon peel, vinegar, salt and garlic. Whisk in olive oil.

## Orange Dressing

*Ingredients*
335ml/12fl oz of fresh orange juice
55ml/2fl oz of olive oil
1 tablespoon of balsamic vinegar
1 teaspoon of salt
1/2 teaspoon of freshly ground black pepper

*Preparation*
Whisk together orange juice, olive oil, balsamic vinegar, salt and freshly ground black pepper in a small bowl.

# Fresh Basil Dressing

*Ingredients*
400ml/13 1/2fl oz of olive oil
1 handful of fresh basil leaves, chopped
juice of 1 lemon
salt and pepper

*Preparation*
Blend all ingredients in a blender until smooth.


# Garlic Dressing

*Ingredients*
1 egg
salt and pepper
3 tablespoons of red wine vinegar
5 cloves of garlic, minced
225ml/7 1/2fl oz of olive oil
115ml/4fl oz of fresh green herbs (chives, parsley, basil, dill)

*Preparation*
In a medium-sized bowl, whisk together the egg,
salt, 1 tablespoon of vinegar and garlic.
Whisk in 1/2 of the olive oil, pouring
slowly.

After dressing thickens, add
the rest of the vinegar and
oil, alternating a little
of each at a time.
Whisk in the
herbs and
pepper.

# Tarragon Dressing

*Ingredients*
170ml/6fl oz of olive oil
juice of 1 lemon
1 tablespoon of red wine vinegar
1 tablespoon of mustard
2 cloves of garlic, minced
1/2 teaspoon of fresh tarragon, finely chopped
salt and pepper

*Preparation*
Blend all ingredients in a blender until smooth.

# Oregano Oil Dressing

*Ingredients*
1 sprig of fresh oregano
1 sprig of fresh thyme
225ml/7 1/2fl oz of olive oil
55ml/2fl oz of balsamic vinegar
salt and pepper to taste

*Preparation*
In a medium mixing bowl combine
the oregano, thyme, oil, vinegar, salt
and pepper.

Mix together and pour into a jar
with a lid. Shake well.

Store at room temperature.

# Mustard Vinaigrette

*Ingredients*
1/4 teaspoon of fresh tarragon, chopped
1 1/2 tablespoons of sherry vinegar
1 1/2 teaspoons of Dijon mustard
2 tablespoons of sour cream
6 tablespoons of olive oil
a pinch of salt

*Preparation*
In a small bowl, mix
together the vinegar, salt,
mustard, tarragon, and sour
cream.

Whisk in olive oil.

# Yoghurt & Blue Cheese Dressing

*Ingredients*
115ml/4fl oz of plain yogurt
2 tablespoons of olive oil
juice of 1 lemon
1 clove garlic, minced
30-60g/1-2oz of blue cheese,
crumbled

*Preparation*
Mix all ingredients in a
blender.

# Roquefort Vinaigrette

*Ingredients*
60-90g/2-3oz of roquefort cheese
6 tablespoons of olive oil
2 tablespoons of sour cream
4 teaspoons of sherry vinegar
a pinch of salt

*Preparation*
Combine cheese, sour cream, and vinegar in a blender. Stir in olive oil and add salt.

# Red Pepper Oil

*Ingredients*
55ml/2fl oz of extra-virgin olive oil
115g/4oz of finely chopped red onion
115g/4oz of finely chopped red pepper
55ml/2fl oz of fresh lemon juice
3 tablespoons of chopped fresh oregano
2 tablespoons of chopped fresh mint
2 teaspoons of salt
3/4 teaspoon of round black pepper
1 finely chopped garlic

*Preparation*
Place all the
ingredients in a jar
with a screw lid and
shake well.

Store in a refrigerator.

# French Dressing No. 1

*Ingredients*
1 cup of sugar
115ml/4fl oz of red wine vinegar
225ml/7 1/2fl oz of olive oil
1 teaspoon of garlic salt
1/2 teaspoon of paprika
pepper
2 teaspoon of onion, minced

*Preparation*
Combine all ingredients in a blender.

# French Dressing No. 2

*Ingredients*
1-1/2 tablespoons of chopped garlic
1-1/2 tablespoons of chopped shallots
55ml/2fl oz of balsamic vinegar
2 tablespoon of Dijon mustard
1 teaspoon of fresh lemon juice
2 salt-packed anchovy fillets, de-boned, soaked in milk to cover for 30 minutes, drained, and patted dry
1 large egg yolk
225ml/7 1/2fl oz of extra virgin olive oil
225ml/7 1/2fl oz of canola oil
Freshly ground white pepper

*Preparation*
Purée the garlic, shallots, vinegar, mustard, lemon juice and anchovies in a blender until smooth. Transfer to a mixer with the paddle attachment and beat in the egg yolk. With the machine running, slowly drizzle in the olive oil and canola oil. Season with white pepper.

Cover and refrigerate. Can be stored in the refrigerator for up to 3 days.

# French Dressing No. 3

*Ingredients*
115ml/4fl oz of fresh lemon juice
340ml/11 1/2fl oz of olive oil
4 clove of garlic, chopped
2 teaspoons of salt
1/2 teaspoon of pepper
1 teaspoon of dry mustard
1 pinch of ground cayenne
75ml/2 1/2fl oz of chilli sauce
1 teaspoon of paprika
2-3 teaspoons of horseradish, if desired.

*Preparation*
Mix all ingredients in a large jar.

Cover and shake until well blended.

Store in refrigerator.

# Caesar Dressing

*Ingredients*
3 tablespoons of sour cream
1 egg, slightly beaten
1 teaspoon of garlic salt
a pinch of pepper
3 tablespoons of olive oil
2 teaspoons of white wine vinegar

*Preparation*
Blend all ingredients in a blender until smooth.

# Basil Mayonnaise

*Ingredients*
1 large egg
1 teaspoon of freshly squeezed lemon juice
75g/2 1/2oz of chopped fresh basil
2 tablespoons of chopped green onions
1 teaspoon of salt
1 teaspoon of fresh ground black pepper
1 cup of olive oil

*Preparation*
Combine the egg, lemon juice, basil, green onions, salt, and pepper in a food processor or blender and purée for 15 seconds. While the processor is running, slowly stream in the olive oil.

When all of the oil has been added, turn off the machine and scrape down the sides and cover. Process again until the mixture becomes a thick mayonnaise. Remove the mayonnaise to an airtight container and refrigerate for at least 30 minutes. Use within 24 hours.

# Olive Oil & Lemon Dressing

*Ingredients*
225ml/7 1/2fl oz of olive oil
55ml/2fl oz of lemon juice
1/2 teaspoon of oregano
or parsley
salt and pepper

*Preparation*
Mix all the ingredients
together and stir well.

Use the dressing immediately in salads, on vegetables and on meat or fish.

# Olive Oil & White Wine Vinegar Dressing

*Ingredients*
225ml/7 1/2fl oz of olive oil
115ml/4fl oz of white wine vinegar
1/2 teaspoon of oregano or parsley

*Preparation*
Put all the ingredients into a blender and mix well.

# Garlic & Walnut Dressing

*Ingredients*
225g/8oz of slightly roasted walnuts
2 cloves of garlic
1 medium onion (optional)
2 tablespoons of finely chopped
parsley or basil
7-8 tablespoons of olive oil

*Preparation*
Put all the ingredients into a
blender and mix well.

This dressing goes perfectly with
pasta.

My Recipes

# My Recipe

*Ingredients*

*Preparation*

# My Recipe

*Ingredients*

*Preparation*

# My Recipe

*Ingredients*

*Preparation*

# My Recipe

*Ingredients*

*Preparation*

# My Recipe

*Ingredients*

*Preparation*

# My Recipe

*Ingredients*

*Preparation*

# My Recipe

*Ingredients*

*Preparation*

# My Recipe

*Ingredients*

*Preparation*

# My Recipe

*Ingredients*

*Preparation*

# My Recipe

*Ingredients*

*Preparation*

Index

# Index